Oxford Phonics World 2

Short Vowels

Kaj Schwermer   Julia Chang   Craig Wright

Workbook

OXFORD
UNIVERSITY PRESS

A Write and say.

a

B Read, check, and write.

1.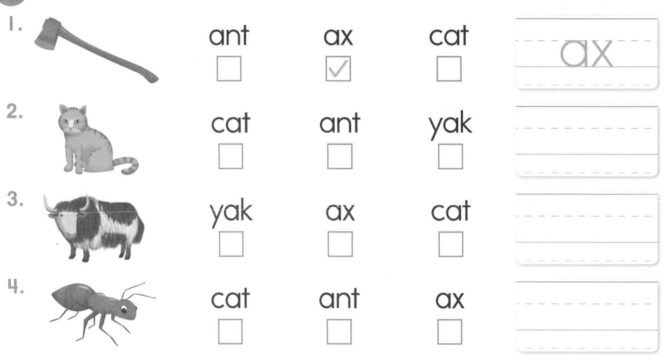

| ant ☐ | ax ☑ | cat ☐ | ax |

2.

| cat ☐ | ant ☐ | yak ☐ |

3.

| yak ☐ | ax ☐ | cat ☐ |

4.

| cat ☐ | ant ☐ | ax ☐ |

C Follow the a sound. Write.

a

short a

a

A Write and say.

a + **m** = am   **r** + **a m** = ram

B Read, say, and check.

1.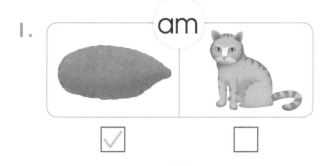
am
☑   ☐

2.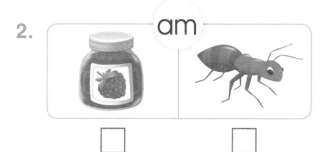
am
☐   ☐

3.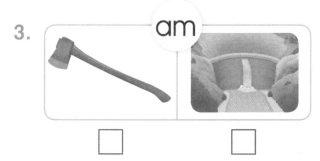
am
☐   ☐

4.
am
☐   ☐

C Do the puzzles.

1. ↓

2. →   d a m

3. ↓

4. →

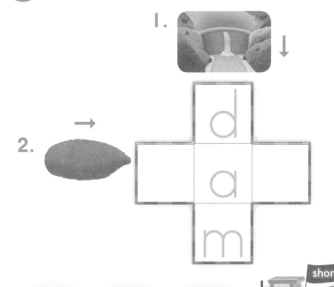
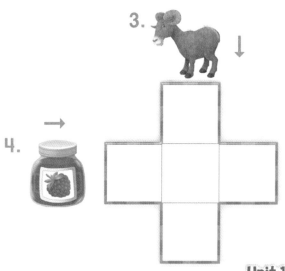

a am **an**

A Write and say.

a + n = ___   f + a n = ___

B Say, circle, and write.

1.    2.   3.   4.

(an) am   am an   am an   an am

 pan    m    f    c

C Find and circle the word.

1.

a (p a n) a m

2.

m a m a n n

3.

f a f a n a

4.

a c a n a m

short a

an

A Read, say, and check.

1. 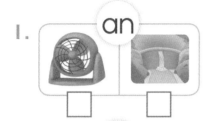 an

2. 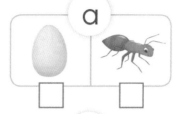 a

3.  am

4. 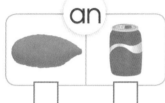 an

5. 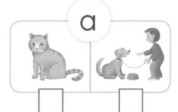 a

6. 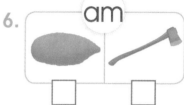 am

B Read, check, and write.

1.  fan ☐ ant ☐ yak ☐

2. man ☐ ram ☐ cat ☐

3.  can ☐ dam ☐ yam ☐

4.  ram ☐ ax ☐ ant ☐

5. yam ☐ fan ☐ jam ☐

6.  dam ☐ can ☐ pan ☐

 a am an

A Write and say.

a + d = ___   d + a d = ___

a + g = ___   b + a g = ___

B Read, say, and check.

1.  ag
☐ ☐

2.  ad
☐ ☐

3.  ad
☐ ☐

4.  ag
☐ ☐

C Unscramble and write.

1. a d d
dad

2. g a r

3. b g a

4. d a p

short a

ad   ag

A Write and say.

a + p = ☐   c + a p = ☐

B Say, circle, and write.

1.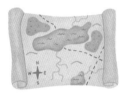

m
n ⟨ap⟩
t

map

2.

c
m ap
t

3.

c
m ap
n

4.

t
m ap
c

C Follow the ap sound. Write.

ad ag ap **at**

A Write and say.

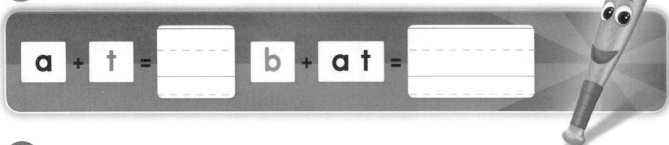

a + t = _____   b + at = _____

B Read, check, and write.

1.
bag ☐   pad ☐   bat ☐   _____

2. cat ☐   rat ☐   ant ☐   _____

3. pan ☐   cap ☐   hat ☐   _____

4. mat ☐   map ☐   man ☐   _____

C Find and circle the word.

1. n a m a t n

2. y a h a t n

3. r a t a h g

4. b a g b a t

short a

at

A Read, say, and check.

1. 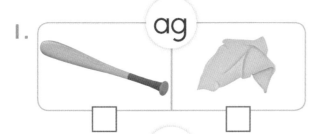 ag
□ □

2. ap
□ □

3. at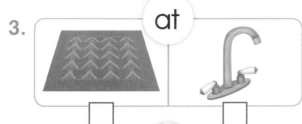
□ □

4.  ad
□ □

5. ap
□ □

6. at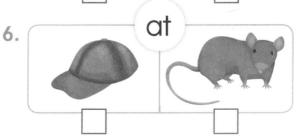
□ □

B Unscramble and write.

1.

p c a

2.

t a b

3.

p a n

4.

g b a

5.

d d a

6.

t h a

A Match the pictures that rhyme.

1.
2.
3.
4.
5.
6.

B Do the puzzles.

1. ↓

2. →

3. ↓

4. →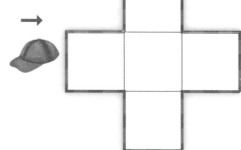

5. 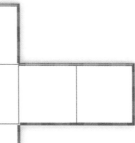 ↓

6. →

7. ↓

8. →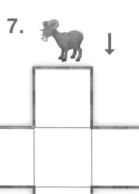

short a

 a am

C Say, circle, and write.

1.

at   ag

r _____

2.

ad   an

p _____

3.

am   an

y _____

4.

at   an

c _____

5.

ap   an

m _____

6.

ag   at

b _____

D Read, say, and check.

1. at

☐   ☐

2. ad
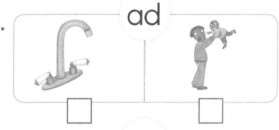
☐   ☐

3. am
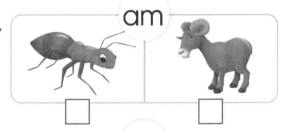
☐   ☐

4. an

☐   ☐

5. ap
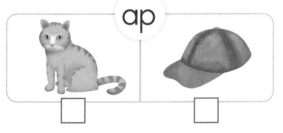
☐   ☐

6. ag
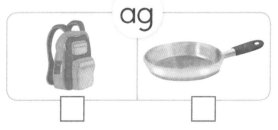
☐   ☐

ad   ag   ap   at

Unit 3   e et en ed

A Write and say.

e

B Read, check, and write.

1. vet ☐   ten ☐   web ☐

2. egg ☐   web ☐   ten ☐

3. ten ☐   vet ☐   egg ☐

4. web ☐   egg ☐   vet ☐

C Follow the e sound. Write.

6

10

e

A Write and say.

e + t = _____   j + e t = _____

B Read, say, and check.

1. 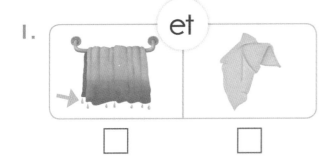 et

☐ ☐

2. 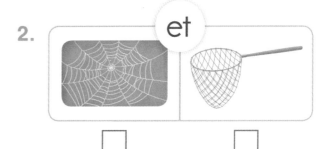 et

☐ ☐

3. 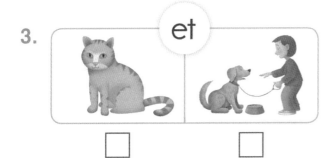 et

☐ ☐

4. 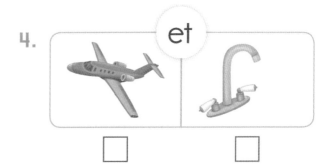 et

☐ ☐

C Do the puzzles.

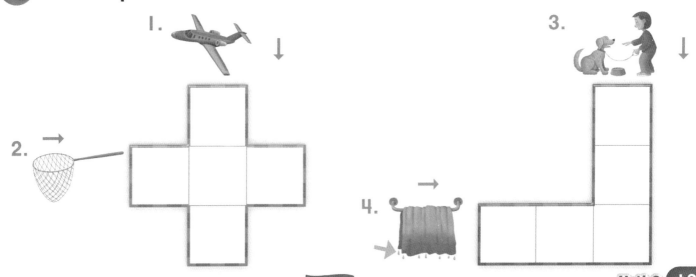

1. ↓

2. →

3. ↓

4. →

short e

et

e et **en ed**

A Write and say.

e + n = ___   h + e n = ___

e + d = ___   r + e d = ___

B Say, circle, and write.

1.
en   ed

p___

2.
en   ed

r___

3.
ed   en

b___

4.
ed   en

h___

C Find and circle the word.

1.

m h h e n n

2.

p e n p n e

3.

f e r e d b

4.

e d a b e d

short e   en   ed

A Read, say, and check.

1. 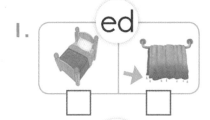 ed
☐ ☐

2. 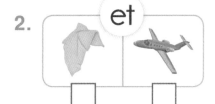 et
☐ ☐

3.  e
☐ ☐

4. en
☐ ☐

5. et
☐ ☐

6. ed
☐ ☐

B Read, check, and write.

1.   web   pen   red
☐ ☐ ☐

2.   ten   jet   vet
☐ ☐ ☐

3.    pet   vet   wet
☐ ☐ ☐

4.   net   hen   web
☐ ☐ ☐

5.   red   wet   egg
☐ ☐ ☐

6.   bed   net   pen
☐ ☐ ☐

A Write and say.

B Read, check, and write.

1. hip ☐   ink ☐   in ☐   _____

2. in ☐   hip ☐   zip ☐   _____

3. in ☐   ink ☐   zip ☐   _____

4. ink ☐   zip ☐   hip ☐   _____

C Follow the i sound. Write.

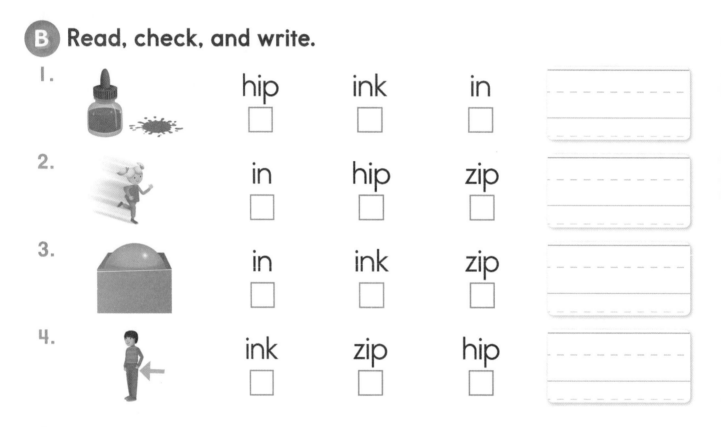

A Write and say.

i + p = ☐   l + ip = ☐

B Say, circle, and write.

1.

h
l   ip
z

_____

2.

s
t   ip
z

_____

3.

k
r   ip
t

_____

4.

r
s   ip
t

_____

C Read, say, and write.

1. You can use your  _____ to  _____ .

2. You can use your  _____ to  _____ .

i ip ib id

A Write and say.

i + b = _____   b + ib = _____

i + d = _____   k + id = _____

B Read, say, and check.

1.  id

☐   ☐

2. ib

☐   ☐

3. ib

☐   ☐

4. 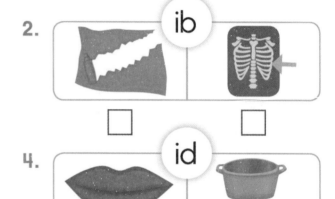 id

☐   ☐

C Do the puzzles.

1. ↓

2. →

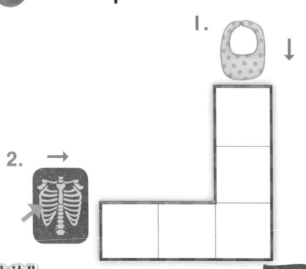

3. ↓

4. →

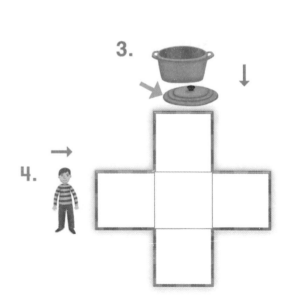

short i

ib   id

A Read, say, and check.

1.  i

2. 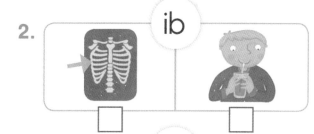 ib

3. 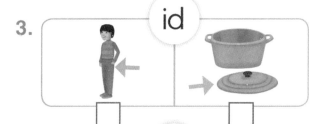 id

4. 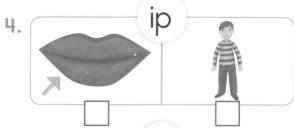 ip

5.  ip

6. 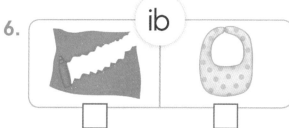 ib

B Say, match, and write.

i ib id ip

1.  • ・

2. 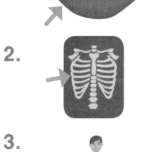 • ・k

3.  • ・

4. 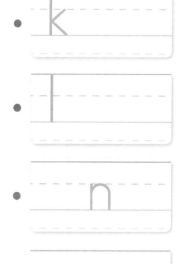 • ・n

・r

 i   ip   ib   id

A Match the pictures that rhyme.

1.
2.
3.
4.
5.
6.

B Do the puzzles.

1.

2.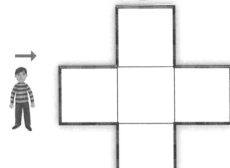

3.

4.

5.

6.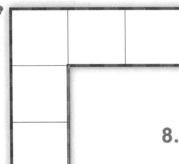

7.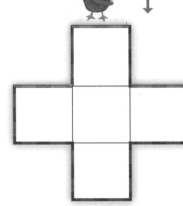

8.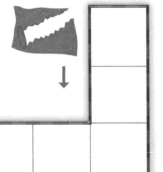

short e

e   et   en   ed

C Say, circle, and write.

1.  ip
ib

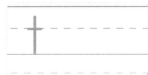

2.  e
i

gg

3.  ib
id

4. ed
et

j

5. en
ed

h

6. ed
et

b

D Read, say, and write.

1. The  _____ is on the _____ .

2. Use your _____ to _____ .

3. I see  _____ in the  _____ .

4. The _____ is on the _____ .

 i ip ib id

A Write and say.

i + n = ___   p + in = ___

B Read, check, and write.

1. bin ☐   fin ☐   pin ☐   _____

2. win ☐   bin ☐   fin ☐   _____

3. pin ☐   bin ☐   win ☐   _____

4. fin ☐   pin ☐   bin ☐   _____

C Do the puzzles.

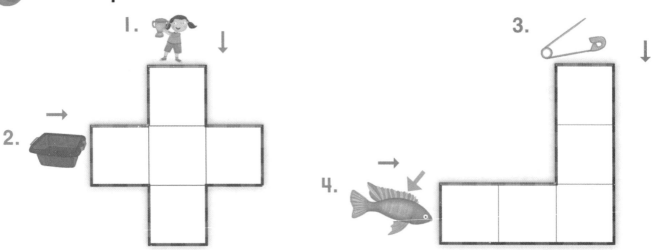

1. ↓
2. →
3. ↓
4. →

short i

in

A Write and say.

i + g = ____   f + i g = ____

B Read, say, and check.

1.  ig

☐ ☐

2.  ig

☐ ☐

3.  ig

☐ ☐

4. 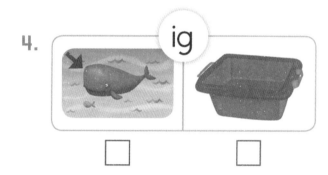 ig

☐ ☐

C Unscramble and write.

1.   2.   3.    4.

g w i   d g i   i b g   g i f

____   ____   ____   ____

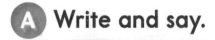

in ig it ix

A Write and say.

i + t = _____   p + i t = _____

i + x = _____   s + i x = _____

B Say, circle, and write.

1.
2.
3.
4.

it ix	ix it	it ix	ix it
m _____	h _____	s _____	p _____

C Find and circle the word.

1.

p i t p i b i

2.

i m i m i x n

3.

i h i t h i g

4.

f i n s i x g

short i

it   ix

A Read, say, and check.

1. 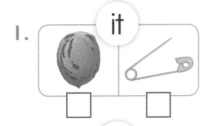 it
☐ ☐

2.  in
☐ ☐

3. 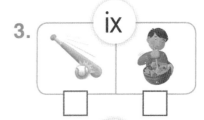 ix
☐ ☐

4. ig
☐ ☐

5. ig
☐ ☐

6. in
☐ ☐

B Read, check, and write.

1.  fig ☐ pin ☐ fin ☐

2.  mix ☐ big ☐ bin ☐

3. fig ☐ pit ☐ dig ☐

4. dig ☐ hit ☐ tip ☐

5. win ☐ wig ☐ bin ☐

6. mix ☐ fig ☐ six ☐

short o

o   ot   op

A **Write and say.**

O

B **Read, check, and write.**

1. rod ☐   log ☐   ox ☐

2. ox ☐   fox ☐   log ☐

3. log ☐   ox ☐   rod ☐

4. fox ☐   ox ☐   log ☐

C **Follow the o sound. Write.**

short o

A Write and say.

o + t = ____   p + o t = ____

B Read, say, and check.

1.  ot

☐   ☐

2.  ot

☐   ☐

3. 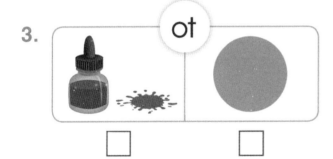 ot

☐   ☐

4.  ot

☐   ☐

C Do the puzzles.

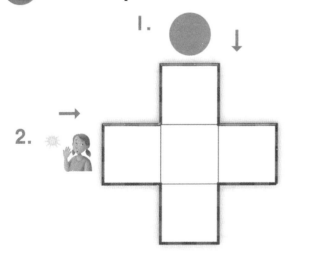

1. 2.

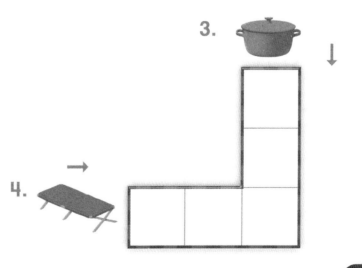

3. 4.

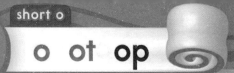

short o

o ot op

A Write and say.

o + p = _____   t + op = _____

B Say, circle, and write.

1.    2.   3.    4.

ot op   op ot   op ot   ot op

m_____   h_____   t_____   p_____

C Find and circle the word.

1.

o h o p p o p

2.

m o t t o p o

3.

b o p o p o d

4.

o b o p m o p

short o

op

A Read, say, and check.

1. o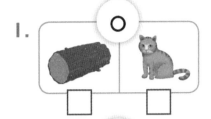

2. op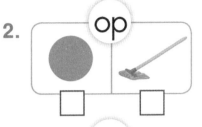

3. ot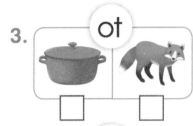

4. o

5. op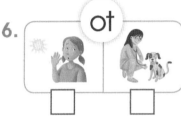

6. ot

B Say, match, and write.

1.  •

2.  •

3.  •

4.  •

5.  •

6.  •

• d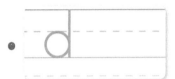

• l

• c

• p

• h

• r

o   ot   op

short i   short o

A Match the pictures that rhyme.

1. 2. 3. 4. 5. 6.

B Do the puzzles.

1. →

2. ↓

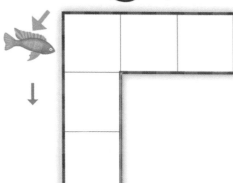

3. ↓

4. →

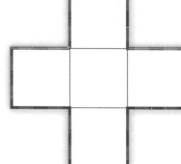

5.  ↓

6. →

7. →

8.  ↓

short i

 in   ig   it   ix

C Say, circle, and write.

1. 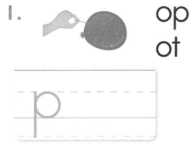 op
ot

_____
p _____

2. ox
ix

_____

3. it
ot

_____
p _____

4. 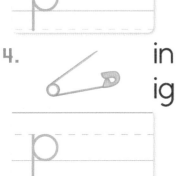 in
ig

_____
p _____

5. 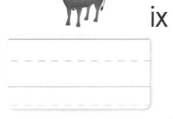 ot
op

_____
p _____

6.  ig
it

_____
b _____

D Say, match, and write.

1.  •

2. •

3.  •

4.  •

5.  •

6. •

•  c

• 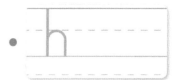 m

• 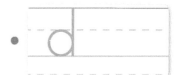 h

•  d

•  b

• r

short o   o   ot   op

A Write and say.

u

B Read, check, and write.

1. sun ☐   up ☐   jug ☐

2. hug ☐   jug ☐   sun ☐

3. up ☐   sun ☐   hug ☐

4. jug ☐   hug ☐   up ☐

C Follow the u sound. Write.

A Write and say.

u + g = _____   b + u g = _____

B Say, circle, and write.

1.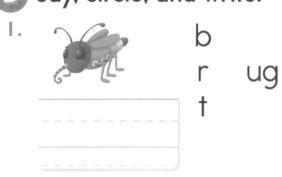
b
r   ug
t
_____

2.
c
j   ug
k
_____

3.
c
p   ug
m
_____

4.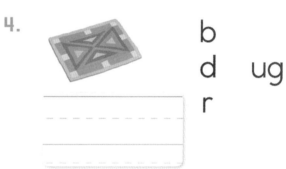
b
d   ug
r
_____

C Find and circle the word.

1.

h u h u g u m

2.

g u m u g b u

3.

l u h r u g u

4.

h u m b u g u

u ug **ud up**

A Write and say.

u + d = _____   b + **u d** = _____

u + p = _____   p + **u p** = _____

B Say, circle, and write.

1.
ud   up
p _____

2.
up   ud
m _____

3.
up   ud
c _____

4.
ud   up
b _____

C Do the puzzles.

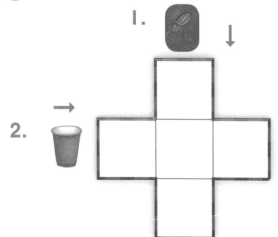

1. ↓

2. →

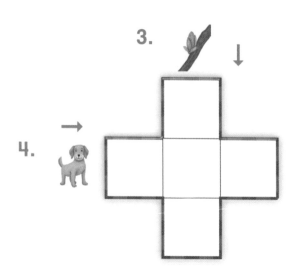

3. ↓

4. →

short u

ud   up

A Read, say, and check.

1. 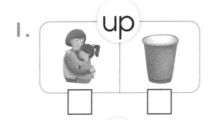 up ☐ ☐

2.  ug ☐ ☐

3. 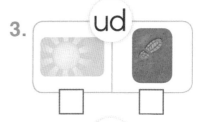 ud ☐ ☐

4. u ☐ ☐

5. u ☐ ☐

6. ug ☐ ☐

B Read, check, and write.

1.   jug ☐   cup ☐   mug ☐   _____

2.   pup ☐   bud ☐   up ☐   _____

3.    mud ☐   rug ☐   bud ☐   _____

4.   bud ☐   pup ☐   hug ☐   _____

5.    sun ☐   cup ☐   rug ☐   _____

6.    jug ☐   mug ☐   mud ☐   _____

u ug ud up

A Write and say.

u + t = _____   n + u t = _____

B Read, check, and write.

1.    cut ☐   nut ☐   hut ☐   _____

2.   nut ☐   hut ☐   cut ☐   _____

3.   hut ☐   cut ☐   nut ☐   _____

C Follow the ut sound. Write.

_____

short u

ut

A Write and say.

u + b = ____   c + u b = ____

u + m = ____   g + u m = ____

B Read, say, and check.

1. um
☐   ☐

2. ub
☐   ☐

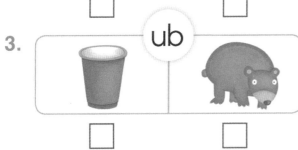

3. ub
☐   ☐

4. um
☐   ☐

C Do the puzzles.

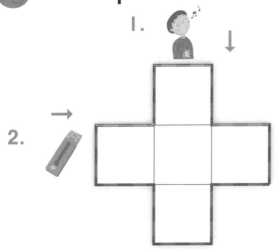
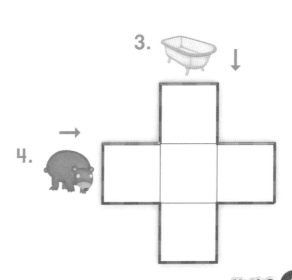

1. ↓

2. →

3. ↓

4. →

ut ub um **un**

A Write and say.

u + n = _____   b + u n = _____

B Read, check, and write

1. 　run　fun　bun
　□　□　□

2. 　run　fun　hut
　□　□　□

3. 　bun　bug　run
　□　□　□

C Say, match, and write.

1. 　•

2. 　•

3. 　•

• r

• f

• b

A Read, say, and check.

1. ut

☐ ☐

2. ub

☐ ☐

3. um

☐ ☐

4. un
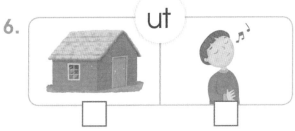
☐ ☐

5. un

☐ ☐

6. ut

☐ ☐

B Unscramble and write.

1.

n u r

_____

2.

t u n

_____

3.

m h u

_____

4.

n u f

_____

5.

t c u

_____

6.

b c u

_____

A Match the pictures that rhyme.

1.
2.
3.
4.
5.
6.

B Do the puzzles.

1.
2.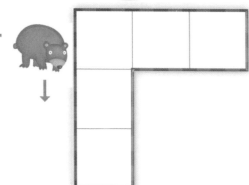

3.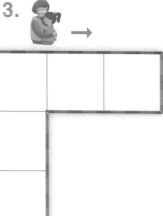
4.

5.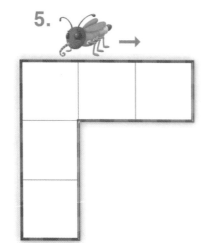
6.

7.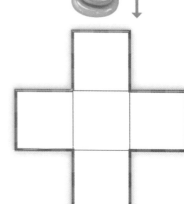
8.

C Say, circle, and write.

1. ug
   up

   p

2. ub
   ud

   c

3. um
   un

   r

4. ut
   ud

   b

5. um
   ug

   b

6. ut
   up

   h

D Read, say, and write.

1. The _____ is in the _____.

2. The _____ is on the _____.

3. He can _____ and eat a _____.

4. I see a _____ in the _____.

ut   ub   um   un

a	am	an
at	e	et
ad	ag	ap
en	ed	i
ip	ib	id
in	ig	it
ix	o	ot

op	u	ug
ud	up	ut
ub	um	un
a	b	c
d	e	f
g	h	i
j	k	l

m

n

o

p

q

r

s

t

u

v

w

x

y

z

These cards
belong to:

_____